by GRAHAM

25 YEARS

25 YEARS

THE HOUND
WHO
KNOWS
IT ALL

Published by Associated Magazines Ltd.
for Mail Newspapers plc.

© 1988 Mail Newspapers plc.

ISBN 0 85144 460 1

Printed by Richard Clay Ltd.,
Bungay, Suffolk.

Distribution by Seymour Press, 334 Brixton Road, London SW9 7AG.
Tel: 01-733-4444. Telex 88-12945.

Fred Basset, whose hound's eye view of life in and around the home has amused millions of Daily Mail readers for 25 years, is commemorated in this special Silver Jubilee cartoon strip book.

Creator Alex Graham has brought together more than 200 strips – from the lovable little rascal's first appearance in 1963 to the present day.

Graham is a Scot, from Dumfries, and was educated at Dumfries Academy and Glasgow School of Art. He became a full-time cartoonist in 1945 and has worked for all the leading British magazines.

At one time he had three weekly strip cartoons, in addition to Fred Basset, published in the Daily Mail but now concentrates principally on that strip.

BASSET, Fred: Born Fleet Street, 1963. Resides in suburbia with two faithful humans. No known relatives except a distant uncle called Bob. Close associates: Yorky, Jock, Big Bruce, Alex Graham. Hobbies: burying bones, frightening cats. Ambition: to catch a rabbit.

At first glance, Fred Basset's biography doesn't look much. Yet this personable hound has millions of fans throughout the world who avidly follow his daily activities through the columns of the Daily Mail, The Mail on Sunday, plus hundreds of other news-papers throughout the world where the strip is syndicated.

In Germany he's 'Wurzel', in Norway 'Lorang', in Finland 'Kioraskoira', but wherever he appears he's met with profound and dedicated affection. He has a regular postbag of fan letters and requests for his autograph, plus presents and cards by the dozen on his birthday and at Christmas. What's intriguing about Fred is that his fans come from all stratas of society from MPs and judges (one of whom considered Fred would make an admirable judge . . .) to old ladies and children. One of his greatest admirers was P.G. Wodehouse with whom Fred's creator, Alex Graham, kept regular correspondence for a number of years. The Fred Basset strip was once dropped from Wodehouse's local paper in America but he successfully campaigned to have it restored . . . In 1978 the Mail responded to Fred's unique

popularity by producing the first Fred Basset calendar – sales soared and it has proved to be a favourite ever since.

Back in 1963 when Fred was born. Alex Graham was already a well-known cartoonist working for newspapers and magazines including the Tatler. He was asked by the Daily Mail to come up with some rough ideas for a family strip cartoon featuring a 'thinking dog'.

Alex cheerfully admits that Fred was in pretty poor shape to start with. He knew very little about basset-hounds and had to go out and buy a book on them. "People wrote in to ask what kind of dog it was supposed to be. When I look back now on my early drawings, it baffles me that I was asked to carry on!" says Alex.

From the beginning, Alex formed a partnership with Leslie Hulme at the

Hardly a ripple to disturb the surface of the water.

Steady, smooth progress...

Daily Mail who has continued to provide the immaculate lettering for the strip. The words that Leslie has lettered have changed in tone over the years. Alex says that Fred used to be rather "common" and didn't always speak that well. "But now I hope he's become more respectable, more dignified as he's matured!" There was also a new challenge six years ago when Fred went into colour when the first "YOU"

magazine was published.

Fred is a character that's difficult to pigeon-hole. There's certainly much more to him than bones and rabbits. "That's only part of his appeal," says Alex. "He comments on and criticises on human behaviour. And I hope he's funny too!"

Alex and his wife, Winifred, once owned a basset – called Freda. She was succeeded by Freda Mark II, but since her

Fluent changes of direction...

And I've never had a swimming lesson in my life...

demise they've had a Yorkshire terrier called Yorky (naturally) and a poodle called Tosh (the surviving half of a pair; the other one was called Mac . . .).

Why not another basset? "I'm very fond of them. They're lovely affectionate creatures, but they're difficult to train!

"If you want a basset to be obedient you have to anticipate what it's going to do and then tell it, nicely, to do it."

Twenty-five years is a long time to be dreaming up and drawing the same strip, but fortunately, it's not something that Alex ever tires of. "I love doing it – it's still a lot of fun for me." And for all of us, too. Happy anniversary Fred! Here's to the next one . . .

1963  1967

FRED BASSET by GRAHAM

What I can't understand is...

...why those new exercises of his...

...which presumably are designed to set him up for the day...

...always result in him coming down to breakfast in a state of near collapse...

747

FRED BASSET by GRAHAM

The half-pound of butter, by all means...tin of custard powder, okay... three packets of soup, I don't mind at all...

812

...small tin of pepper, fine...¼ lb. of mushrooms, no trouble at all...

...It's the half-stone of potatoes that's killing me...

1968  **1972**

FRED BASSET
by GRAHAM

1298

FRED BASSET
by GRAHAM

1299

1973 1978

FRED BASSET
by GRAHAM

2305

Ah, here comes Basil... He looks a little like me, I'm told

Which isn't surprising, really... We're vaguely related!

He's a distant cousin on my mother's side...

GRAHAM

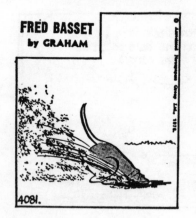

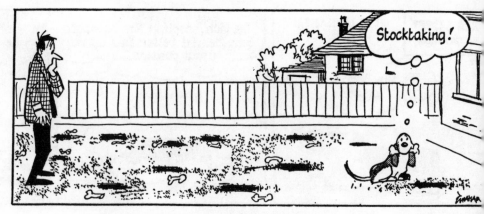

FRED BASSET
by GRAHAM

4407.

What a team! Yorky up front as a striker, Jock controlling the mid-field, me sweeping up at the back...

... and big Lofty, safe as houses, in goal!

FRED BASSET
by GRAHAM

4416

I feel absolutely MISERABLE when they go out and leave me on my own

However, a lovely fire and a nice soft armchair...

There's nothing like a little comfort for making misery easier to bear

1979 1983

FRED BASSET
by GRAHAM

And now a photographer from our local newspaper...

4649

This freak potato of his is certainly creating a lot of interest

FRED BASSET
by GRAHAM

FOOD, FOOD! IT'S ALL YOU SEEM TO THINK OF...**FOOD!**

5198

I'M HUNGRY! WHAT'S FOR LUNCH?

FOOD, FOOD! DOESN'T **ANYBODY** THINK OF ANYTHING BUT FOOD AROUND HERE?

I think she's a little over-tired today

FRED BASSET
by GRAHAM

5259

The new people are moving into No. 2....I'll have a look....

I'm not a snob, but one can tell the type of person by their furniture

They'll do!

1984 1988

FRED

FRED BASSET by GRAHAM

5757.

WAIT!...THERE'S SOMETHING WRONG WITH FRED!

I can't move! I've seized up!

HE'S GOT HIS FOOT ON HIS EAR!

Well, so I have! Silly me!

That's a relief!...I thought I'd been struck by some form of paralysis!

GRAHAM

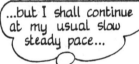

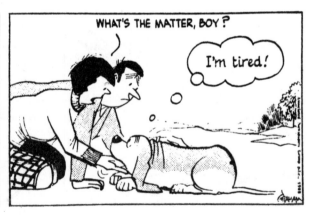